TREATING DEPRESSION NATURALLY

By
Magna Parks, Ph.D.

TEACH Services, Inc.
Brushton, New York

2007 08 09 10 11 12 · 5 4 3 2 1

Copyright © 2007 TEACH Services, Inc.
ISBN-13: 978-1-57258-467-9
ISBN-10: 1-57258-467-X
Library of Congress Control Number: 2007924453

Published by

TEACH Services, Inc.
www.TEACHServices.com

CONTENTS

PREFACE

I have worked as a psychologist for almost 18 years. In my work with various clients, I have become increasingly aware that what I had been taught in my years of psychological training was insufficient to adequately treat the many mental disorders that plague our society today. One of these disorders is depression, which is becoming very prevalent both in the United States and abroad. Recently, I have learned that there is "another way" to treat depression, one that addresses the "whole" person. The information I have acquired about this come from the fields of medicine, neuroscience, psychology, and religion. As I have begun to use the principles and concepts from these areas, my work with clients has taken a positive turn. Of course, not everyone who comes to me for treatment is ready or willing to incorporate these principles—many prefer the traditional approach to treating depression. But, for those who are courageous enough to try something "different," the results have been impressive! Even though I have only been applying these principles for a relatively short time period, I felt compelled to share what I have learned in this booklet. I must acknowledge that some of the concepts presented in this book are those that I acquired while working for almost a month with an internal medicine physician who has revolutionized the treatment of depression—Dr. Neil Nedley. Prior to this, I applied a few lifestyle strategies in treating clients with emotional disorders. However, my work with Dr. Nedley taught me how to do so in a more systematic manner. For several years, he has successfully applied lifestyle principles in the treatment of depression and the results have been phenomenal!

It is my hope that as you read the enclosed information that you will be courageous enough to implement the principles that are presented in your life. I assure you that these concepts will change your life and you will see that there is "another way" a more natural approach to help you or someone you love overcome depression. If you incorporate these principles, you will not only feel better, but will BE better. Try them—you will never be the same!

ACKNOWLEDGMENTS

I would first like to thank God, for without Him the writing of this book would not have been possible. After God, the most important person in my life is my husband, Al Parks. I am so grateful for his love, support, and encouragement as I have made significant changes in my work as a psychologist and for his constructive criticism as I wrote this book. I thank Dr. Neil Nedley for giving me the opportunity to learn more about how to effectively treat depression. I am also grateful to Dr. Agatha Thrash for her kindness and for taking time out of her busy schedule to carefully edit my work. In addition, I thank Dr. Samuel Koranteng-Pipim for being one of the first individuals to help me appreciate how important it is to write books. I also thank my family—my parents, Everard and Sarah James, and my brother, Lloyd James for their encouragement and prayers. Finally, I have to say "thanks" to several friends—Rochelle Narain, Melissa Summers, Yolanda Innocent-Palmer, Doris McLarin-Hicks, Maggie and Moses Mason, Jeremiah and Aretha Davis, James Luke, Olive Jones, and others who encouraged me and expressed excitement as I worked on this project. This book is dedicated to each one of these individuals—again I say, thank you!

CHAPTER 1

UNDERSTANDING DEPRESSION

D-E-P-R-E-S-S-I-O-N. What comes to mind when you hear this word? Sad feelings? Feelings of being "down" or "blue?" Most, if not all, of us experience these emotions at some point in our lives. Typically, we have these feelings as a result of change, loss, or just "everyday living." The response of sadness or unhappiness in such situations is appropriate and tends to be only temporary in nature. However, when these emotions persist and start to impair one's life, this may indicate the presence of clinical depression. The Diagnostic and Statistical Manual of Mental Disorders, Fourth Version (DSM-IV), which is the psychiatric handbook most often used in diagnosing mental disorders, indicates that **major** depression involves a group of symptoms that cause significant distress or impairment in one's general functioning.[1] These symptoms include the following:

- Deep sadness on most days (irritability may be present in children and adolescents)
- Total or very noticeable loss of pleasure or interest in all or almost all activities
- Significant increase or decrease in appetite, weight, or both
- Sleep disturbance, either sleeping too much or too little
- Increased restlessness/agitation or intense slowness (observable by others)
- Fatigue or loss of energy
- Feelings of worthlessness or excessive or inappropriate guilt
- Diminished ability to think or concentrate, or indecisiveness
- Recurrent thoughts of death or suicidal thoughts

1

In order to be diagnosed with major depression, one must experience **five or more** of the previous symptoms during a **2-week period** and they must represent a **change** from previous functioning. In addition, one of these five symptoms **must be** *either* **depressed mood** *or* **loss of interest or pleasure in activities.**[2]

Some individuals may not fit the above criteria which suggest that they do not have major depression. However, there are several other types of depressive disorders. These include, but are not limited to, situational depression (depressive symptoms attributed to a recent emotional trauma or loss), bipolar depression (severe mood swings, from extreme "lows" to extreme "highs"), and dysthymic disorder (chronic depression that occurs for at least 2 years). In order to obtain an accurate diagnosis of your depression, it is suggested that you seek the professional opinion of a medical doctor or mental health professional.

The Alarming Prevalence of Depression:

How prevalent is depression? A few years ago, the surgeon general called major depression an "epidemic" in America. According to the National Institute of Mental Health (NIMH), about 20.9 million American adults, or about 9.5 percent of the U.S. population age 18 and older in a given year, have a mood disorder (which include the three major types of depressive disorder).[3] The World Health Organization has found that major depression is the leading cause of disability worldwide among persons aged 15–44 years old.[4]

As we can see, depression is a "real" illness. Unfortunately, many don't realize this. The impact and devastating effects of depression has been minimized by many who do not understand it. Too often I have heard comments such as "it's all in their heads" or "they need to just shake it and move on" or even "just focus on the positive and forget the negative." The overall view seems to be that people who are depressed are somehow "weak" or "inadequate." As a result, many people who suffer from this illness shy away from seeking help for fear of how they may be viewed by others. A 2002 article in the *Journal of the American Medical Association* indicates that most individuals with depression receive no treatment for their symptoms. The authors of this article also point to a recent surgeon general report that states the promotion of treatment for people with depression is MORE of a problem than developing effective treatments.[5] If you, dear reader, are one of those individuals who have not sought help for your depression OR who has tried the standard treatment approaches and still suffer with this illness, know that there is hope. Please read on!

CHAPTER 2

"I'VE TRIED EVERYTHING—
WHY AM I STILL DEPRESSED?"

Typically, when a person suffers from depression, he or she is referred for medication and/or counseling. Let us consider each of these treatment options. The first professional that most depressed individuals will see is their physician. In most cases, the first (and sometimes only) form of treatment recommended by the physician is antidepressant medication. Medications have been found to be helpful in alleviating many depressive symptoms. Some are effective for a few weeks and others are effective for several years. However, the use of medication also has several drawbacks which may include negative side effects, lack of effectiveness (either in the beginning or after a person has been on the medication for a long time), and possible negative long-term effects.

The second standard treatment option used for depression is counseling. Many physicians will refer their patients for counseling to be utilized in conjunction with, or sometimes instead of, medication. Typically, counseling involves the use of what is known as "talk therapy." For many years, as a psychologist, I used this approach for treating clients who suffer from depression. The focus of my work was to help them understand how events of the past, such as negative childhood experiences, and/or events in their current life have "caused" their depressive symptoms. This was based on the assumption that gaining "insight" or understanding about these events is necessary to overcome depression and most emotional/mental disorders. It is true that past and current situations contribute to depression. However, talking about these situations/events may help a depressed person "feel" better, but does not necessarily help them "get" better. Some reading this statement may disagree because their experience with therapy (whether they are patients or therapists) has appeared to be beneficial. Counseling can be helpful, to a limited extent. However, in my 18 "plus" years as a psychologist, I have seen many clients "recycle" in and out of traditional psychotherapy. Some of these individuals also had a history of taking one or more antidepressant medications (or were currently taking them). But, they continue to struggle with chronic or sporadic episodes of depression. So, what is the answer?

Depression: A Different Perspective

The standard forms of depression treatment previously mentioned tend to address the **symptoms** and not the **causes** of depression.[1] In light of this, those who utilize these traditional treatment strategies will likely experience a recurrence of their depressive symptoms at some point in their lives. Dr. Neil Nedley, an internal medicine physician, reviewed scientific and medical literature and found that there are numerous factors that can cause depression (for further information on this, consult his book, *Depression: The Way Out*). Most of the causes of depression point to lifestyle habits, which are largely ignored by medical and mental health professionals. Through a series of events, one of which was the opportunity to personally work with Dr. Nedley, I have learned that to adequately treat depression, I have to help people learn better habits of living. These lifestyle habits are helpful because they target the functioning of our brains (as well as our nervous system). The brain is the "seat" of the mind, and if it is working properly, then we can be more assured that our emotional and mental functioning will be enhanced. By altering our lifestyle habits not only can we increase our effectiveness in treating depression, but we can also be more successful in preventing it from occurring or recurring in the future. This is the focus of this booklet. If you suffer from depression, know that you do not have to be dependent on medication and counseling for the rest of your life. There is a better way!

CHAPTER 3

EIGHT PRINCIPLES THAT WORK!

"Pure air, sunlight, abstemiousness, rest, exercise, proper diet, the use of water, trust in divine power,—these are the true remedies."[1]

These words were penned in the early 1900's by health educator and author, Ellen G. White, who many believe was inspired. In this quote, she delineates what are known as "eight natural remedies" that can be used to treat many of the illnesses that plague our world today. Since the time that she shared this insightful information, scientific research has confirmed (and continues to confirm) that much of the diseases that we suffer from have to do with our lifestyle habits. Diet, exercise, sleep, and other habits of living can be deciding factors in determining the health of our bodies and our minds.

A handy acronym for these eight natural remedies is N-E-W-S-T-A-R-T, which was coined over 25 years ago by health professionals at Weimar Institute, a health facility that focuses on teaching lifestyle strategies to treat various illnesses.

A break down of this acronym is as follows:

N is for "nutrition"
E is for "exercise"
W is for "water"
S is for "sunlight"
T is for "temperance"
A is for "air"
R is for "rest"
S is for "sleep"
T is for "trust in God"

The use of these remedies in the treatment of various illnesses has been successfully utilized by numerous health professionals in various outpatient settings as well as residential health facilities, such as Weimar Institute. However, one of the first persons to systematically apply the use of lifestyle strategies in the treatment of depression was Dr. Neil Nedley. I have had the privilege of working with Dr. Nedley as a counselor in one of his 19-day residential treatment programs for depression. My work with him greatly contributed to my learning how to better utilize lifestyle strategies for treating not only depression, but other mental disorders. Let us now consider each of these "remedies" and explore how they can be helpful for those who are suffering from this illness.

CAUTION: The following information will likely be helpful for most cases of depression, but not all. There are some cases of depression that may require professional medical help. Thus, it is advised that before implementing this program, readers should get a thorough medical exam to rule out any medical cause for their depressive symptoms. A medical exam is also recommended to assess a person's current physical functioning to determine if there are any aspects of this program that should be avoided or approached with caution. In addition, if you are currently using antidepressant medication, please DO NOT stop taking it on your own. If you choose to implement the following lifestyle strategies, work with your doctor to determine how and when you can reduce and eventually eliminate the use of medication.

CHAPTER 4

NUTRITION—GOOD FOOD, GREAT MOOD!

"It cannot be too often repeated that whatever is taken into the stomach affects not only the body but ultimately the mind as well."[1]

Most people who seek treatment for depression from physicians and/or mental health professionals are rarely questioned about their dietary habits. The thought that what we take into our stomachs can have an impact on our minds, as mentioned in the above quote, is something that is often not considered. However, increasing evidence is revealing that a poor diet has an impact not only on physical health, but on mental health as well. The main organ of the mind is the brain. In order to function properly, the brain must be properly nourished. Ellen G. White, the same inspired author who introduced the lifestyle principles that is the focus of this booklet, states: "Every organ of the body requires its share of nutrition. The brain must be supplied with its portion...."[2] If the brain does not receive adequate nutrients, it will not function as well as it can. This can lead to a number of emotional and mental problems, which may include depression.

Serotonin Can be Increased Naturally

Serotonin is a brain chemical that regulates several psychological functions, including mood, anxiety, aggression, impulse control, and thinking abilities. It has been found to play a central role in depression. Serotonin is one of many neurotransmitters produced by our brains. A neurotransmitter is a chemical produced by our nerve cells that transmits signals from one nerve cell to another. Many of the more commonly prescribed antidepressants work because they increase the effective use of serotonin in the brain. As mentioned in a previous section, medication can be useful for the treatment of depression. However, there are some disadvantages to relying on medication such as unwanted side effects, possible ineffectiveness, and even unknown long-term effects from taking these drugs.

Believe it or not, we can increase the production of serotonin without the use of medication. One of the ways that this can be done is through the foods that we eat. For example, in order for serotonin to be produced in our brains, trytophan, an amino acid, must be present.[3] Trytophan is considered the "raw material" that the brain uses to make serotonin. The lack of trytophan in our diets can contribute to depression. In fact, one recent study showed that the depletion of trytophan in the brain caused increased sadness, which is one of the hallmark symptoms of depression.[4] By eating trytophan-rich foods we can naturally boost levels of serotonin.[5]

Foods that have significant amounts of tryptophan include the following:

> Almonds, wheat, kidney or lima beans, oats, pumpkin seeds, sesame seeds, black walnuts, spinach, cabbage, black-eyed cowpeas, whole grains, avocados, and tofu.

Carbohydrates Can Be Helpful for Depression

In recent years there has been a lot of "hype" about low-carbohydrate diets, such as the Atkins diet. These diets have been effective for many in causing some initial weight loss. However, there is evidence that suggests that diets such as this can lead to depression. Dr. Judith Wurtman and her colleagues from MIT have found that when you stop eating an abundance of carbohydrates, your brain slows down the production of serotonin.[6] Some nutrition/health professionals even refer to carbohydrates as "brain fuel" because they produce glucose, the main source of energy for the brain. So, carbohydrates are an important brain food that should not be excluded from our diets.

"Good" versus "Bad" Carbohydrates

It is important to know that there are certain types of carbohydrates that are more useful for the brain than others. An example of a carbohydrate source that is not very helpful for brain function is refined sugar, which has been stripped of its naturally occurring vitamins, minerals, and other nutrients. This type of sugar provides a burst of energy due to a dramatic rise in blood sugar (or glucose) levels—which is one of the reasons many depressed people consume a significant amount of sugary foods. This is followed by an equally dramatic fall in blood sugar levels, which can later result in problems with irritability, foggy thinking, anxiety and other related symptoms. It has also been shown that after the intake of refined sugar, the brain takes another 45 to 75 minutes to regain optimal intellectual functioning after the blood sugar returns to normal.[7] The best types of carbohydrates are those that are ingested in their natural state—namely, fruit, grains and certain vegetables. These are known as "unrefined" carbohydrates. It is these types of food that provide fuel for the brain and contribute to the production of serotonin.

The following are examples of unrefined carbohydrates:

Broccoli, brown rice, potatoes (in their natural state), blackberries, wheat pasta, winter squash, whole grain breads.

Case Example:

An interesting case example of how these healthy carbohydrates can help with depression is that of a 21-year old depressed female I treated 3 or 4 years ago. At the time that she came in, I was just beginning to understand the relationship between nutrition and depression. This client had been suffering from depression for several years. In an attempt to help her, I utilized most (if not all) of the psychological techniques I knew, but nothing was very successful in alleviating her symptoms. One day, I mentioned to her that there is evidence that certain foods can be helpful for depression. After sharing the little I knew about this, I encouraged her to increase her consumption of whole grain foods, vegetables, and fruit. After a couple of weeks, there was a noticeable difference when she came in to see me. Specifically, she seemed more cheerful and less irritable. She reported to me that she was feeling better. However, after a few weeks, she resumed her usual eating habits and fell back into what she called a "slump." We talked about the apparent impact of healthy foods on her depression. She tried several times to resume her intake of these foods, but never became consistent with this eating pattern. My guess is that if she had continued eating these unrefined carbohydrates for a few months, we would have seen a significant decrease in her depression. In addition, if I knew back then what I know now, we would have tried other natural approaches to address her depression and to help her consistently implement a more healthy diet.

Essential Fatty Acids and Depression

Essential fatty acids are necessary fats that our human body cannot manufacture and, thus, must be obtained from the foods we eat. Two of the fatty acids that are very important for brain functioning is omega-3 and omega-6. Research has shown that depressed people tend to have lower omega-3 fatty acid levels than non-depressed individuals.[8, 9] Omega-6 deficiencies can also contribute to depression. However, the consumption of omega-6 fatty acids (found in vegetable oils such as corn, safflower, sesame, and sunflower oil) is much more common, especially in the American diet, than that of omega-3 fatty acids. The low ratio of omega-3 to omega-6 has been found to contribute to depression.[10] Thus, to effectively combat depression, it is important that one's diet is balanced in the intake of these two fatty acids—with special care being taken to ensure that one is getting adequate amounts of omega-3.

Fish and Depression: What is the "Truth?"

One of the most well-known sources of omega-3 fatty acids is fish. As the importance of omega-3 in the diet has been more publicized, many have touted the benefits of eating fish. However, according to the Physicians Committee for Responsible Medicine, there are several disadvantages to eating fish as a source of omega-3 which are as follows:

- The high amounts of fat and cholesterol and the lack of fiber make fish a poor choice.
- Fish is often high in mercury and other environmental toxins that have no place in an optimal diet.
- Omega-3 in fish oils (supplementary form) are highly unstable molecules that tend to decompose, and in the process, unleash dangerous free radicals.[11]

Given these concerns, the best form of omega-3 is found in vegetables, fruit, seeds and beans.

Some specific foods that are good sources of omega-3 include the following:

> Ground flaxseeds, hempseeds, walnuts, some dark leafy green vegetables (such as collards, kale, mustard greens, spinach, etc.), several legumes (mungo, kidney, navy, pinto, etc.), avocadoes, wheat germ oil, cold-pressed canola oil, safflower oil, and soybean oil.

Case Example

One of my more recent cases was a woman who reported phenomenal results by increasing her intake of omega-3. This client was so depressed that she had to take a short-term leave of absence from her job. When she came in to see me, I immediately began to share with her various lifestyle tips. As she began to implement these lifestyle strategies, she reported some reduction in her depression. However, it wasn't until she added omega-3 to her diet (in the form of 3-4 tablespoons of ground flaxseeds per day) that she began to experience a significant change in her depressive symptoms. A few weeks after she returned to work, she called me and excitedly shared how she was calmer, less moody, and was concentrating better. Her co-workers even noticed the difference and several of them began to use the flaxseeds as well! Now, it should be added, that this may not result for everyone who adds this nutrient to their diet. However, it is just one example of how omega-3 can contribute to the effective treatment of depression.

Vitamin Deficiencies Can Increase Depression

There is some evidence that a deficiency in certain vitamins can contribute to depression. One such vitamin is folic acid (vitamin B-9). Folic acid deficiency is one of the most common vitamin deficiencies in the United States. The results of several studies show that low levels of folic acid are correlated with depression and other problems with mental functioning.[12, 13, 14, 15] There is also evidence that patients with low folic acid levels tend not to improve with the use of standard antidepressants.[16, 17]

The following foods are excellent sources of folic acid:

Beans and legumes (chickpeas, black-eyed cowpeas, lentils, navy beans, red kidney beans), citrus fruits and juices, wheat bran and other whole grains, dark green leafy vegetables (such as mustard greens, and spinach), okra pods.

Folic acid is one of several B-complex vitamins. These vitamins are essential for the proper functioning of our nervous system and are crucial for mental and emotional well-being. There are health professionals who believe that deficiencies in B-complex vitamins other than folic acid can lead to various depressive symptoms, such as vitamins B-1 and B-6.[18] In one study, it was found that elderly women with vitamin B-12 deficiencies were twice as likely to be depressed, compared with women who had normal levels of the vitamin.[19] It is advised that if one is concerned about possible B vitamin deficiencies, he or she should have vitamin levels tested by their family physician to rule this out as being one of the possible causes of their depression.

Food sources of various B-complex vitamins include:

Fortified breads and cereals, whole grains, avocadoes, legumes, and some green vegetables

---

Saturated Fats May Contribute to Depression

Some health experts believe that the over-consumption of saturated fats contributes to depression. This is based on the idea that foods high in saturated fat interfere with blood flow to the brain by causing the arteries and small blood vessels to become blocked and the blood cells to become sticky and clump together. This results in poor circulation of the blood to the brain which can cause sluggishness, slow thinking, and fatigue—all symptoms of depression.[20] Examples of foods high in saturated fat include animal products and fried foods. Even though there is limited, if any, research evidence to support the relationship between saturated fat and depression, it would not hurt to reduce the intake of dairy products, meat products, and fried foods for overall better "brain health".

Plant Foods Combat Depression:

An overview of the above nutrients suggests that there are four major food groups that are critical for combating depression: fruit, vegetables, nuts/seeds, and whole grains. This highlights the importance of using more plant-based foods for optimal mental health. Some may balk at the idea of reducing or eliminating animal products from their diet. My response is merely this: if you are suffering from depression, try to increase the intake of plant foods and decrease animal products in your diet. Monitor your mental/emotional functioning and see if you observe any difference in your depressive symptoms. These foods are not at all harmful to your health and they are delicious! It is worth the try!

Case Example

One of my patients is a 30-year old woman who suffered with depression for at least 12 years. She came in to see me and reported that she had been in and out of therapy for the past 10 or so years. I shared with her that I utilize lifestyle strategies for treating depression. She expressed interest in trying this approach. This client began to make many of the nutritional changes previously discussed in this section. After almost two months, she came in and reported that many of her depressive symptoms had significantly decreased. She also added that this is the "best" she has felt in her "whole life." As of the writing of this book, she continues to do well and has told me that she no longer needs to attend therapy and now understands how to better manage her depression!

PRACTICAL APPLICATION:

Now that you have been bombarded with all these nutritional recommendations for treating depression, how can you put it all into practice? Here are a few suggestions:

- Review your standard diet—a simple way to do this might be to chart what you eat for the next 3 or 4 days.

- Review the types of foods that can be helpful for combating depression. Determine how much omega-3 fatty acids, trytophan, and B-complex vitamins (especially, folic acid) are included in your diet.

- Make a decision to choose at least two foods in each group that you will commit to adding to your diet every one or two weeks.

- If you are using a lot of saturated fats, consider how you can gradually eliminate these foods from your diet. A suggestion may be for you to take out one of these foods each week or every other week.

- Realize that making these dietary changes may not be easy, but is possible. Planning ahead is VERY important when you are making these changes. You may want to consider making weekly menus ahead of time. Or, when you go out to eat, you may want to start learning more about healthy foods that are available at different restaurants. Try calling the restaurant ahead of time to plan your menu.

- Commit yourself to start making these changes this week!

Chapter 5

EXERCISE: WALK YOUR WAY
OUT OF DEPRESSION!

This is the second lifestyle area in the NEWSTART plan for living. There is increasing evidence in the medical literature that exercise is helpful for treating depression. Studies reveal that exercising 30 minutes to an hour at least three times a week can be very effective in relieving mild to moderate depressive symptoms - in fact, it has even been shown to be about as effective as antidepressant medication.[1, 2] Even smaller amounts of activity—as little as 10 to 15 minutes at a time—have been shown to improve mood in the short-term.[3]

How Exercise Affects Depression

There are a variety of explanations on how exercise can reduce or relieve depression. For one, it has been suggested that exercise positively affects the levels of certain neurotransmitters, such as serotonin, in the brain. Some health experts also report that it raises endorphins (a "feel-good" chemical) in the brain. Others suggest that exercise reduces the levels of cortisol, a stress hormone, and reduces tension in muscles, which can induce a more relaxed state of being. All of these benefits from exercise can help a depressed person experience enhanced mood, reduced stress and tension, and enhanced sleep (this latter effect has a direct relationship with depression, which we will discuss in more detail later in this booklet).

Case Example

In my work with clients who are depressed, I can cite numerous examples of how consistent, regular exercise contributed to a reduction in depression and even provided motivation to engage in other lifestyle strategies for treating depression. For example, I worked with a woman who had tried various antidepressant medications and had attended traditional therapy several times in the past. When she came in to see me, she was quite depressed. Initially, she had a difficult time implementing many of the lifestyle changes I recommended to her. I encouraged her to exercise and she decided to walk for 15-20 minutes a day. When she came in after two weeks of exercising, she reported a significant change in her depression. As we continued working together, she also recognized that when she missed just one or two days of exercise, she was more sad, irritable, and less able to focus. As this client consistently exercised, she became more motivated to change other aspects of her lifestyle, which were initially hard for her to do. In time, her depression was greatly improved!

Which Type of Exercise Is the Best?

Some may be asking, which is the best type of exercise for combating depression? It is possible to obtain benefits from almost any type of physical activity. Remember, *some* exercise is always better than *no* exercise. Most of the research that has been conducted on exercise and depression focuses on aerobic activities. This is a type of exercise, typically performed at moderate levels of intensity for extended periods of time, which increases your heart rate and improves the body's use of oxygen. The aerobic exercise that is the most simple to engage in is walking. There are many benefits to walking, such as:

- It does not cost anything
- It puts less "wear and tear" on any body parts or joints
- It can be done almost anywhere at anytime
- It can be engaged in by anyone, no matter their age, size or fitness level

There is actually one type of exercise that may prove even more beneficial than walking—that is, mind-engaging exercise.[4] Examples of such exercise include gardening or other vigorous yard/outside work, such as building, chopping wood, etc. These exercises, in addition to raising serotonin production and reducing stress hormone levels, have the added benefit of providing a sense of purpose and accomplishment. This can be very helpful for depressed individuals who feel inadequate and powerless in their lives. Engaging in such activities can also be a good source of distraction for these persons because it can reduce their self-focus, which can help with their negative thinking. However, if there is no such work available, another activity that will help reduce self-centeredness is to become a volunteer in a hospital, nursing home, school, etc.

PRACTICAL APPLICATION

If you have not exercised consistently (or at all) in the past OR if you used to exercise but have not done so in a long time, the idea of starting an exercise program can seem quite overwhelming. On the other hand, some people can easily start exercising, but find it a challenge to be consistent and regular with their program. Here are some tips that may help:

- Start out small. Set simple goals when you begin an exercise program. For example, you can set a goal of walking around your block at lunch time or walking for 5 or 10 minutes/day for a few days. The smaller the goals that you start out with, the less daunting will be the challenge to start exercising.

- Don't overdo it. If you start out with strenuous exercise, you are likely to get very sore and fatigued. This may discourage you from continuing. It is best to engage in mild forms of exercise and build your strength and endurance for more intense exercise over time.

- Consistency is the key! It is better to walk for 10 minutes several days for several weeks, than for 1 hour one week and another hour 2 weeks later.

- If you find that doing the same exercise all the time is monotonous, vary your exercises. For example, you can walk three times a week and try another exercise (such as bicycling or strength-training exercises) on the other days of the week.

- Don't let "feelings" dictate your decision to exercise. Remember, feelings are not reality. The idea of using the "I don't feel like it" reason to avoid exercise (or other things that are good for you) can prevent you from changing our habits. Challenge yourself to rise above your feelings and go for it!

- An exercise partner can be invaluable to your exercise program, as it is less likely that two people will use an excuse at the same time. However, one must be cautious in becoming too dependent on another person for exercise. It is advisable to develop one's own internal motivation for exercising, even if one has a partner.

***CAUTION: Individuals over 40 who have not exercised much in the past and/or those who have medical conditions (such as heart disease or diabetes) should consult with their medical doctor before starting any vigorous exercise program.

CHAPTER 6

WATER—DRINK AND BATHE
YOUR WAY TO HEALTH!

The third lifestyle area in the NEWSTART acronym is water. There is little, if any, research on the use of water for alleviating depressive symptoms. However, any one who has some knowledge about the physiology of the body will recognize the importance of water for optimal physical and mental health. The human brain is approximately 75 to 80% water. Thus, an adequate intake of water is essential for the brain to function properly. One of the systems of our body especially dependent upon water is that of the circulatory system. When water is ingested, it is received in the blood and increases the volume of the blood. The thinner the blood, the better it can circulate throughout the body and do the work that it needs to do, such as carrying nutrients to, or removing waste products from the body.[1] This work is important for all the organs of our body to work properly, including the brain. In fact, one physician states that a "mild degree of chronic dehydration contributes to a mild and chronic depression of mental abilities."[2] If the mental abilities are "depressed," this will result in foggy thinking, concentration problems and other mental difficulties that can be indicative of depression. Most health experts believe that we should drink about eight glasses, eight ounces each, of water per day.

Case Example

I have several clients who have experienced positive results when they increased their water intake. One example of this was my work with a 16-year old female who appeared to be mildly depressed. This young lady was very active and, as a result, received a lot of exercise, fresh air, and sunlight. However, she rarely drank water and typically quenched her thirst with soda and/or juice. Upon my recommendation, she began to increase her water intake. To be honest, I suggested that she drink more water because she had been complaining of chronic headaches. But, as she began to drink more water, we both also observed a decrease in her depressive symptoms. After about 4 or 5 more sessions, she reported to me that she was feeling much better and stated that she no longer needed to come in to see me. I cannot say for sure that her depression was "cured" by increasing her water intake. However, it seems apparent that it did contribute to a decrease in her depressive symptoms.

The use of water is not only helpful internally, but also externally. This is known as hydrotherapy. The use of hydrotherapy for treating mental disorders is not new. For example, in 1927 a medical doctor at the American Medical Association meeting indicated that it is effective in treating "excited mental cases."[3] One specific hydrotherapy treatment found to be beneficial for depression is the contrast shower. This treatment involves alternating hot and cold water in the shower. It stimulates the nervous system and the circulation of blood, both of which can be helpful for depression.

PRACTICAL APPLICATION:

If you have not been drinking sufficient water, make it a goal to start increasing your water intake. Here are a few suggestions:

- Drink 1–2 eight-ounce glasses of water as soon as you awaken in the morning.

- Try to drink at least 2 or 3 glasses between meals and 2 glasses a few hours before going to bed.

- If you find that it is difficult to remember to drink water, keep a water bottle or glass out in your view (both at home and at work) as a reminder.

You may also consider trying a hot-cold shower. As a precaution, if you know that you have a health condition, you may want to consult your health care provider before engaging in this procedure. The following steps can be followed for the hot-cold shower:

1) Begin with the hot water and raise it to as hot as you can tolerate (be careful not to burn or scald yourself). Hold it there for 3 minutes.

2) Turn the valve quickly to full cold. Hold for about 30 seconds. If it is initially difficult to switch immediately to cold water, you can gradually move from hot to cold over a period of 60 seconds. As your body adjusts to this, you should soon be able to switch immediately from hot to cold.

3) Do 3 complete cycles of hot and cold, finishing with the cold water.

4) Dry well, briskly rubbing the skin with your towel. Afterwards, it is **imperative** that you rest for at least 30 minutes in bed. Make sure your body is kept warm and comfortable.

5) For those who are severely depressed, this treatment must be done 2 times a day for 7 to 10 days. Once the depressive symptoms are less severe, decrease the treatment to once each day. When depression is no longer present, three treatments per week should be done for at least six months.[4]

CHAPTER 7

SUNSHINE—LIGHT UP YOUR LIFE!

The fourth lifestyle principle for treating depression involves obtaining adequate sunlight. There is increasing evidence that sunlight can be very beneficial for combating depression. You may now be asking, how can this be when we have been warned for years that exposure to the sun can cause skin cancer? What researchers are now discovering is that the risk of skin cancer increases with *prolonged* exposure to the sun. A moderate amount of exposure to sunlight, however, can be very beneficial for our health, both physically and mentally. For example, a landmark study in 2002 revealed that sunlight significantly increases serotonin, while dark or cloudy days deplete serotonin levels.[1] This should make sense to us when we consider that we tend to feel more cheerful on sunny days than on rainy or cloudy days. Most, if not all, my clients who suffer from depression are strongly encouraged to spend at least 15–30 minutes in the sun per day. Many of them report that this practice leads to a slight, but noticeable, improvement in their depressive symptoms.

Sunlight and Melatonin

Another benefit of sunshine as related to depression is that it regulates the production of melatonin. Melatonin is a hormone that is secreted (generated and discharged) by the pineal gland in our brain. One of its many roles is that it controls the body's circadian rhythm. Circadian rhythms are the daily signals produced by our body that controls various functions such as body temperature, the way other body systems function, sleeping, and waking. The level of secretion of melatonin by the pineal gland is heavily influenced by sunlight. If one fails to get adequate sunlight during waking hours, melatonin production can be greatly reduced.[2] This, in turn, can upset our circadian rhythm. It should also be noted that melatonin production can also be disrupted if we get too much light at night, because it is darkness that stimulates its release.

Sunlight Helps Seasonal Depression

There is a specific type of depressive disorder known as *seasonal affective disorder* (SAD) that has been clearly associated with reduced sunlight exposure. This disorder occurs during the winter months, when the days are shorter and there is less sunlight. If you typically experience depression that starts in September/October and ends in April/May, you may have SAD. Remember, if light has a direct impact on melatonin production and our circadian rhythm, it would make sense that the reduced sunlight during the winter days can lead to increased depression.

Even if one does not have SAD, insufficient exposure to sunlight during any time of the year can lead to problems with depression. Before the invention of electricity, people lived by the sun. They awoke when the sun rose and went to bed shortly after it went down. However, in our more modern society, the sun has little, if anything, to do with how we live our lives. We are spending more time indoors, in the office and at home, and less time out of doors. With the knowledge that sunlight is important for serotonin production during the day and melatonin production during the night, it is clear that a lack of adequate exposure to the sun can reduce the production of these hormones. This can lead to depression. It is also important to note that our circadian rhythm can also be impaired if we do not have regularity in our lives with other activities, such as sleeping, eating, exercising.

Bright Light Therapy and Depression

There is scientific evidence that suggests that exposure to bright light, better known as "bright light therapy," is effective for treating seasonal affective disorder (SAD) and other depressive disorders.[3, 4, 5] During the winter months, it is difficult to obtain bright light in the morning because the sun rises later and many people get up and/or leave their homes before this time. This is especially problematic for those who have SAD. One way to address this problem is to use what is known as a light box. This is a piece of equipment that simulates the brightness of the sun in an indoor setting. It can be used almost anywhere, at anytime of day. If you are interested in using a light box, it is recommended that you consult a health care professional who has knowledge and experience in its usage. However, prior to purchasing this equipment, it may be helpful to try getting natural sunlight some time during the morning hours and monitor how effective this is in alleviating your depression.

PRACTICAL APPLICATION:

The following are recommendations that can help you benefit from sunlight each day:

- To reset your internal body clock, try to go outside into direct sunlight within 10 minutes after sunrise for about 30 minutes.

- Whether or not you have problems with your circadian rhythm, try to get at least 15 minutes of direct sunlight daily. One idea to help you do this might be to go outside on sunny days during your lunch hour.

- Try to exercise in the sunlight—in this way you can "kill two birds with one stone" (obtain exercise and sunlight).

- Remember, prolonged exposure to the sun over a long period of time increases the risk of skin cancer—moderate exposure is best.

***It should be noted that darker-skinned people (such as African Americans) are more tolerant of sun rays than fairer-skinned individuals (such as Caucasians). Thus, they may be able to stay out in the sun for a longer period of time.

CHAPTER 8

TEMPERANCE—"YES," "NO," OR "THAT'S ENOUGH"

"True temperance teaches us to dispense entirely with everything hurtful and to use judiciously that which is healthful."[1]

The fifth lifestyle principle in the NEWSTART acronym is temperance. The Random House Dictionary defines temperance as "self-restraint in action, statement, etc."[2] The concept of temperance has to do with learning how to exercise restraint or self-control. The above mentioned quote reveals that when we exercise self-control we will stay away from things that will harm us and will use healthful things in a wise, balanced manner. This idea is not very prevalent in our society. Television, movies, music, and other sources today encourage us to engage in any activity that our "hearts" desire. In fact, those who seek to refrain from certain actions or who exercise self-control in different areas are usually branded as "extremists" or "weird." Whatever our personal reaction is to this concept, it is one that cannot be ignored when we consider our physical and mental health.

The idea of exercising self-control is very important in the treatment of depression. In my work as a psychologist, I have noticed that many persons who are depressed tend to eat a significant amount of "junk food" such as sweets, potato chips and other forms of refined carbohydrates. When I suggest to these individuals that it would be helpful for them to reduce the consumption of these foods, the majority of them balk at this because they feel it will be too difficult or even impossible to do. It is true that many depressed persons crave these foods because of the burst of energy they receive when they consume them, as discussed in the previous chapter on nutrition. However, their response also suggests to me that the idea of temperance or self-control is a concept that they have either ignored or have not considered. I can say that those who are able to follow the recommendation to reduce or eliminate these and other harmful foods report a noticeable change in their depressive symptoms.

Alcohol, Caffeine, and Nicotine

Another area of temperance that must be considered is the use of what I call the three most "accepted" drugs in society—caffeine, alcohol, and nicotine. In the 19th and early 20th centuries there was an organized effort to encourage moderation or complete abstinence in the use of alcohol. This was known as the "temperance movement." The idea of abstaining from nicotine as well as other substances such as alcohol and caffeine is not very popular in our society. Typically, it is considered relevant only for those who have specific illnesses or problems that necessitate abstinence, such as lung cancer or alcoholism. However, there is evidence that these substances are harmful in general and can lead to physical and mental health problems. Over 100 years ago, E.G. White, health teacher and writer, made the following comments about coffee, tea, tobacco, and liquor:

> "The influence of coffee is in a degree the same as tea, but the effect upon the system is worse. Its influence is exciting, and just in the degree that it elevates above par it will exhaust and bring prostration below par."[3]

> "Tobacco produces an effect on the system fully as harmful as liquor. It stimulates for the time being, but when its immediate influence is gone, those who have used it sink as far below par as they have been elevated above it."[4]

Both of these quotes were written several years before medical science began to discover the harmful effect of these substances. Notice that she states that the use of coffee and tea (caffeine), alcohol, and tobacco excites and then leaves one feeling worse than prior to usage. Could the latter state be referring to a sense of being "down" or "depressed?" Let us now see what contemporary evidence shows about the relationship between the use of these substances and depression.

Alcohol and Depression

Not all heavy or long time drinkers will become depressed. However, alcohol has been found to increase the severity and frequency of depressive symptoms. The results of one study showed that the concentration of serotonin in the blood of subjects after they drank alcohol was similar to patients diagnosed with depression. These findings suggest that the mechanism of depression after alcohol drinking may be related to decreased serotonin in the blood.[5] Statistics show that up to 40% of people who drink heavily will have symptoms that resemble a depressive illness.[6] However, when these same people are not drinking heavily, only 5 percent of men and 10 percent of women have symptoms meeting the diagnostic criteria for depression.[7] In addition, there is some evidence that there is an increased risk for suicide among those who are alcohol-dependent.[8] It appears that many people who suffer from depression turn to alcohol in the belief that it will help ease their symptoms. In my work with clients who are depressed, several of them have admitted that their depression either led them to start drinking and/or increased their alcohol usage. Others report they have been drinking for years before they were diagnosed with depression. I have shared with many of these individuals that alcohol is classified as a "depressant." Depressants initially produce calm, relaxed feelings. However, over time they trigger many of the symptoms that are typical of depression which include impaired concentration, increased crying, sadness, and other related effects. Thus, the use of alcohol actually sabotages any efforts that these individuals make to rid themselves of their depression.

Smoking and Depression

In general, research suggests that there is a reciprocal relationship between depression and smoking in that depression can lead to smoking and smoking can increase the risk of depression.[9, 10, 11] For example, one study found that adolescents who are heavy smokers are more likely to grow depressed and those who have persistent depressive symptoms are more likely to increase their smoking over time. There is also evidence that smokers have decreased brain blood flow, which could predispose them to depression.[12]

Caffeine and Depression

Caffeine is probably the most socially accepted drug in our society. In fact, it is considered "safe" when it is consumed in low to moderate amounts. When I work with individuals who are depressed I almost always inquire about their caffeine usage. Many are surprised to find out that caffeine can "unbalance the mind" because it upsets the delicate balance of nerve transmission in the brain, which can lead to various psychological disorders.[13] The results of one study, for example, revealed that women who were heavy coffee users exhibited a significant increase in suicide risk.[14] Typically, individuals who contemplate or attempt suicide are depressed. In my work as a psychologist, several of my clients, both males and females, have reported a significant improvement in their depression when they eliminated the use of caffeine.

There are some who propose that mild to moderate caffeine usage helps reduce depression. Reportedly, there have been studies that confirm this hypothesis. It is feasible that the use of caffeine, which is a stimulant, can lift the mood of a depressed person because it provides a quick burst of energy. But, it is also feasible that this stimulation can be followed by depressed symptoms that are the same or worse than before the use of caffeine—which is suggested by the previously mentioned quote about the use of coffee and tea by E. G. White. It should be mentioned that caffeine is present not only in coffee and tea, but in certain sodas, chocolate and even some medications.

Case Example

An example of the impact of caffeine usage and depression is the case of a 24-year old female with whom I worked. This client appeared to display symptoms that suggested her depression was in the mild to moderate range. When she came in to see me, she was drinking several cans of caffeinated soda every day. I suggested that she gradually reduce her caffeine usage, which was initially very hard for her. She experienced "caffeine-rebound" headaches for about a week. After another week, she began to report that she felt considerably better. A couple weeks later, she went to see her neurologist, who told her that she appeared less depressed. She came in for a couple of additional sessions and then told me that she no longer needed therapy. Interestingly, this was the ONLY lifestyle change that she made!

PRACTICAL APPLICATION

If you use or overuse alcohol, nicotine, or caffeine and have made the decision that you will like to reduce or eliminate these from your life, recognize that it may not be easy. But, it can be done! There are certain things you can do to help in this process. They are as follows:

1) Make your decision to quit final. Then reinforce it by throwing away everything that pertains to your habit. Leave nothing around to tempt you. Make a decision to no longer buy anything related to your habit.

2) Make a list of the advantages to not engaging in the destructive habit you are trying to eliminate and review this list periodically.

3) Drink lots of water, which helps to flush out impurities. It will also help with caffeine-rebound headaches, which some people experience when they quit using caffeine. In addition, use water on the outside of your body. Bathing or showering at least twice a day, ending with a cold dash or sponge, is especially helpful when quitting smoking.

4) Eat wisely. This should include eating nutritious foods that will help the brain (review nutrition chapter in this book) and even avoiding spicy foods. Also, do not eat when you feel restless and nervous.

5) Increase your exercise. This will reduce weight gain and will also help you relax when you feel tense.

6) Get proper sleep. This will give you the energy you need to "fight" as you seek to eliminate the use of these substances.

7) Seek spiritual help for power to overcome the destructive habit.

8) Don't give up. When things were going against the Allies during World War II, Winston Churchill, the prime minister of Great Britain, was asked about the possibility of surrender. His reply: "Never give up, never give up, never, never, never, never."[15]

NOTE: The above are just suggestions. You may need the support of a professional who has some training in using lifestyle techniques. In addition, there are certain addictions (such as chronic alcohol abuse) that **require** medical help. Please consult a health care provider before you implement any of these steps to determine if you will need help and medical supervision as you seek to eliminate the use of these substances.

CHAPTER 9

AIR—BREATHE YOUR WAY TO HEALTH!

"Air, air…will bless you with its invigorating influence if you will not refuse its entrance. Welcome it, cultivate a love for it, and it will prove a precious soother…at the same its influence is decidedly felt upon the mind, imparting a degree of composure and serenity."[1]

The sixth lifestyle principle that we will focus on is fresh air. The above quote reveals that air can have a soothing effect on our minds. Many of us take this precious commodity for granted and don't recognize how important it is for our mental health. The air that we breathe is electrically charged – that is, it is made up of negative and positive ions. The more negatively charged the air, the healthier it is. The proportion of negative ions is highest in the natural environment, especially around trees, mountains and moving water such as oceans, rivers, and waterfalls. This is why we feel so refreshed and energized when we are around moving water, in a forest, or near the mountains. The air is also very negatively charged after a lightning storm—lightning discharges large amounts of negative ions in the air. There is evidence that the ionization of the air that we breathe has an impact on our mental/emotional functioning. For example, studies have indicated that a high concentration of negative ions is essential for high energy and positive mood.[2] There is also evidence that suggests negative ions can provide relief for seasonal and non-seasonal depression.[3, 4]

Modern-Day Lives and Fresh Air

The typical modern-day lifestyle does not provide us with fresh, ionized air. Air conditioning, lack of ventilation, tightly-insulated buildings, and pollutants destroy negatively charged air. It is nice that we have advanced in knowledge on how to keep our buildings cool during the summer and how to have more energy-efficient homes. However, there has been a "down" side to this advancement in that we are getting less fresh air into our living or working spaces. Thus, many of us live in and constantly breathe "re-circulated" air. And, for those who are depressed, this can be quite detrimental.

Proper Breathing and Fresh Air

Another factor that prevents us from getting adequate air is lack of knowledge on proper breathing. Depressed people, in particular, may breathe shallowly and/or may have poor posture, which does not allow them to get the air that they need. A lack of fresh air to the brain prevents it from functioning optimally. And, as mentioned earlier, if the brain is not working properly, it decreases the chances of overcoming depression.

PRACTICAL APPLICATIONS

How do we ensure that we get adequate fresh air? Here are some suggestions:

- Open windows at home or at work whenever possible. Yes, this should be done even during winter months! When it is cold outside, you can still slightly open your windows to encourage the circulation of fresh air.

- If you do not have windows in your office, take frequent breaks in fresh air.

- Whenever you can, go outside and breathe the air while it is raining or immediately after a thunderstorm.

- Learn how to maintain proper posture. Check your posture throughout the day to ensure that your head and back are erect and that your shoulders are not drooping.

- Try to get away into nature and/or country areas as often as you can.

- Take deep breaths whenever you exercise.

- Practice proper breathing. Here is a breathing exercise that may help:

  • Stand erect, outside or near an open window
  • Place hands one on top of the other on your upper abdomen
  • Breathe in slowly, allowing your chest and abdomen to expand
  • Hold for a count of 20
  • Breathe out slowly, hold for a slow count of 10
  • Repeat 10 times
  • Do this exercise at least 5 times a day

*Tip—this can be done while walking or engaging in any other type of exercise.[5]

Case Example:

One of my clients was a 43-year old male who suffered from anxiety and depression. One of the first lifestyle changes we focused on to help him was teaching him how to breathe properly. Initially, it was difficult for him to implement the above mentioned breathing technique. However, as he began to become more adept at this, he noticed that this had a significant impact on not only his depressive symptoms, but his symptoms of anxiety as well. He was especially excited about this strategy because it helped him cope more effectively with stressful situations that, in the past, would trigger many of his depressive symptoms. He reported to me that when he is faced with these situations, he now takes time to engage in deep breathing and has found that it has helped him better cope with stress and feel less depressed.

CHAPTER 10

REST—GOOD REST MAKES YOU THE BEST!

"Proper periods of sleep and rest…are essential to health of body and mind."[1]

The seventh lifestyle principle important to understand for treating depression is rest. It doesn't take much to realize that we are a "sleep-deprived" society. Statistics show that we sleep on average 6.9 hours per day, almost an hour less than a few decades ago. The reasons that many sleep less range from busy schedules, overwork, increased options for "night-time" entertainment, and problems with falling and staying asleep. Many do not recognize that, as cited in the quote above, sleep is "essential" for us to have healthy minds (and bodies). Studies show that there is a reciprocal relationship between depression and sleep. For example, a study of about 8000 subjects revealed that the risk of depression among those who had insomnia was significantly higher than those who had no insomnia.[2]

Getting To Bed Early Can Help With Depression

Proper sleep is important in addressing the problem of depression. It has been found that the human body needs about 7 to 8 hours of sleep per night. However, what is even more important is the time of night within which we obtain these hours of sleep. There is a critical time period during the night when the body/brain restores and heals itself, which is about two or so hours before midnight. This is probably the reason that E. G. White stated that, "Two hours good sleep before twelve o'clock is worth more than four hours after twelve o'clock.[3] It is also important to note that the production of melatonin increases at nighttime and peaks at around 2 o'clock in the morning. Melatonin, which was discussed earlier in this book, is a hormone that, among other things, helps us get restful sleep at night.

Unfortunately, the modern lifestyle is one that does not encourage early bed time, somewhere between 9:00 and 10:00 pm. Most of us are awake and exposed to light at this time of night, which negatively affects the release of melatonin. A prolonged pattern of staying up late at night can have detrimental effects on our health, which include problems with depression. I typically tell people who consider themselves to be "night owls" or who have difficulty falling asleep because of their depression that they should get in the bed early, whether or not they fall asleep right away. At least they will obtain some benefits from resting and being in darkness with their eyes closed. Then, as they start to implement some of the other lifestyle principles, they will probably find that they will have decreasingly less difficulty falling asleep—unless there are other factors, such as the presence of a sleep disorder, that is the cause of their sleep problems.

Regularity Is Important

Over 100 years ago, E. G. White indicated that "there should be regular hours for rising...for meals, and for work".[4] This quote highlights the importance of regularity. Many of us do not realize that our body CRAVES regularity. When we engage in activities such as sleep in an inconsistent, irregular manner, this disrupts our circadian rhythm. One of the reasons that this happens is because our bodies may end up releasing melatonin and other biochemicals at the wrong time, which can cause sleepiness during the day and sleeplessness at night. Unfortunately, many people don't realize this and engage in activities that prevent them from having regular sleep/wake routines. Over a prolonged period of time, this can lead to various physical and even mental disorders, such as depression.

Shift Work and Depression

One special group of people who are particularly vulnerable to depression resulting from a disrupted circadian rhythm is shift workers. These individuals have irregular or rotating work-shift hours, which leads to irregular sleeping, eating, and other activities. This can lead to a variety of mental and physical disorders.

Case Example

A middle-aged female was referred for counseling by her physician, who diagnosed her with mild depression. This woman worked as a highway patrol officer and had a chronic history of sleep problems that began about three years earlier. She reported that she had been evaluated by several physicians, none of whom could determine the cause of her sleep difficulties. When she came to my office, an evaluation of her history revealed that she had engaged in shift work for at least half of her career. At the end of our first session, I shared with her my clinical impression that her problems were due to a disrupted circadian rhythm. We talked about strategies she could use to restore her circadian rhythm, which included the use of a light box (discussed in an earlier section in this booklet). This client decided to purchase a light box and within a couple of weeks, she no longer had problems sleeping.

Other Reasons for Sleep Problems

It should be mentioned that there are several factors that can lead to poor sleep other than what has been previously mentioned. For example, sleep can be disrupted by the use of substances such as caffeine, alcohol, or nicotine (especially in the evening or at night), eating less than 4 hours before bedtime, stress/anxiety, anger, boredom, certain medications, inadequate exercise, and engaging in stimulating activities in the evenings, such as watching entertainment television. Recent studies have also found a relationship between sleep disorders and depression. For example, a Stanford University School of Medicine study found that people with depression are five times more likely to have a breathing-related sleep disorder, such as sleep apnea, than non-depressed people.[5] When I work with persons who suffer from depression, I will question them on the aforementioned factors to determine how we can tailor a plan that will enhance their sleep.

PRACTICAL APPLICATION:

Given the above information on sleep and depression, it is strongly recommended that those who are seeking to treat their depression naturally should work on making sure they get the most out of their sleep. Here are some tips:

1) To address circadian rhythm problems, implement the following:

> - Try to get to bed by no later than 10 p.m.

> - Sleep in a dark, cool environment (to enhance melatonin release).

> - Sleep in the same room, same bed every night.

> - Get about 30 minutes of sunlight no later than 10 minutes after sunrise. You may also want to consider using a light box. Contact a health professional with knowledge of its use for further information.

2) Keep bedroom free of noise and disruptions (like TV).

3) Allow yourself time to get 7–8 hours of sleep.

4) Don't watch the clock during the night – this will increase your anxiety and prevent you from relaxing enough to fall back asleep.

5) Don't use alcohol, tobacco, or caffeine 3–4 hrs. before going to bed.

6)   Eat a light supper (for example, whole fruit) and do so 3–4 hrs. before bedtime. Or, try not eating supper at all!

7)   Exercise in the afternoon or evening. Take care not to exercise too close to bedtime. Exercising can be stimulating and may make it hard for you to fall asleep.

8) Don't toss and turn. Lie still when you get in bed, even if you feel restless.

9)   Try to keep active during the day to reduce boredom.

10) Prepare yourself to go to sleep. Engage in pre-bedtime activities to condition your mind to "unwind" and relax before you go to bed. For example, take a warm bath, listen to calming music, read spiritual material, etc. This will prepare you (mentally and physically) to fall asleep.

11) Don't engage in any other activities than sleep in bed. This will help condition your mind to relax when you get in bed and not stay alert enough to read a book or watch TV.

12) Avoid stimulating activities, such as watching movies or entertainment TV, and/or reading romance, mystery, or fiction books before bedtime. These activities reduce your ability to relax.

13)   Don't take a nap during the day. If you are sleepy, engage in an activity that will help you stay awake.

14) Try to stay away from chemical sleep aids because you can become dependent, especially if you use them for a long period of time.

If none of the above methods are helpful, you should see a health care professional to rule out other possible causes for your sleep problems, such as a sleep disorder or other medical condition.

CHAPTER 11

TRUST IN DIVINE POWER

This is the final lifestyle principle in the NEWSTART plan for treating depression. Some of you reading this booklet may be surprised that a focus on spirituality would be included in a lifestyle program for depression. However, the idea of incorporating a spiritual component in a treatment program is not new. Most of us are familiar with Alcoholics Anonymous (AA), a self-help program for alcoholics. Whether or not you agree with all of the underlying assumptions of AA, it is hard to deny that a large part of its success is due to its focus on the need for a "higher power." Many people with whom I have spoken has shared with me that the spiritual component of the AA program was most vital in helping them overcome and maintain their sobriety.

There are an increasing number of health care professionals who recognize that spirituality is important for good mental health. The scientific literature even presents evidence of an association between spirituality and psychiatric disorders, which include depression. For example, several studies suggest that spirituality helps recovery from depression and that depression is lower among those who are spiritually focused and personally devoted to their religion.[1, 2, 3] It should be mentioned that the type of spirituality that has been found to be the most beneficial is that which is based on a firm, inner belief or faith.[4, 5] This is a type of religiosity that can be contrasted to spirituality or religion that focuses more on religious forms, such as church attendance and church participation. The implication of this finding is not to downplay religious activities, but to emphasize that that those who are depressed (and even those who are non-depressed) are more likely to benefit from a spirituality that is relevant and personal in their lives. This type of religious experience is one that leads to trust and belief in what a "divine power" can do on a personal level, which is the focus of this eighth lifestyle principle.

Trust Is Important for Depression Recovery

What is trust and why is it important? Trust is defined as "unquestioning belief in the integrity, strength, or ability of a person or thing."[6] The trust that is the focus of this lifestyle principle is one that is directed to a divine power. It is a strong belief that we can rely on the "integrity, strength, and ability" of this power to help us overcome our difficulties. When one believes in such a power, this can provide the strength needed to implement the lifestyle changes that will help with depression. This is important because many of the suggested changes can be difficult and challenging. The idea that we have a "power source" that we can access for help should empower and encourage those who are seeking to overcome their depression. Even more important, this concept of trusting in a divine power underscores the belief that it is this supernatural power that actually provides true and complete recovery from this illness.

Who do we trust? The answer to that question lies in one's standard for determining truth. My belief is that this standard of truth is the Bible. When the term "divine power," is used, it is referring to God, who is the focus of the Bible. Ellen G. White, the woman author who wrote about these lifestyle principles, also refers to the same when she used the phrase "trust in divine power." In fact, it should be mentioned that this author (and others who ascribe to her work) believes that these principles were developed by God Himself, who in turn shared them with her—which is what is meant when she is referred to as an "inspired" author.

The Bible and Depression

Are there any benefits from reading or studying the Bible if one is trying to overcome depression? Actually, there are many. One is that reading the Bible enhances an understanding of who God is. The greater knowledge one has of Him, the better one can "trust" in the power that He offers to overcome depression.

Another benefit is that there are many principles that can be extracted from the Bible that can be useful in dealing with depression. Consider the following texts:

"A merry heart doeth good like a medicine, but a broken spirit drieth the bones." (Proverbs 17:22).

"For as he thinketh in his heart, so is he..." (Proverbs 23:7)

"...whatsoever things are true, whatsoever things are honest, whatsoever things are just, whatsoever things are pure, whatsoever things are lovely, whatsoever things are of good report. If there be any virtue, if there be any praise, think on these things." (Phillipians 4:8)

These texts highlight the principle that our thoughts/mental attitude can have an impact on our health, both physically and psychologically. This concept is one that is becoming more widely recognized in the field of psychology. In the last 20 or so years, there has been increasing evidence that depression, and other psychological disorders, can be treated by helping people change their negative or distorted thoughts. The standard type of treatment used to address this is known as "cognitive behavioral therapy." The goal of this therapy is to help people understand and change their negative thinking. For example, many depressed people frequently think about or verbalize negative things about themselves or others. Cognitive behavioral therapy helps these individuals to recognize and change these negative thoughts. This approach has been found to be very beneficial for helping people overcome their depression. And, as revealed in the above quoted texts, the principle that we are affected by what we think, was introduced in the Bible hundreds of years before cognitive behavior therapy was discovered. With this in mind, it is my belief that the Bible, when it is used practically, can be a very effective tool for helping people change their thoughts and overcome their depression.

The Bible can also be helpful in dealing with depression because it can be a source of encouragement and hope. There are many promises in the Bible that can inspire and uplift, which is sometimes very helpful during the "dark days" of a depressed person's life. Here are examples of some of these promises:

> "Thou wilt keep him in perfect peace, whose mind is stayed on thee; because he *trusteth* in thee." (Isaiah 26:3)

> "For with God, nothing shall be impossible." (Luke 1:37)

> "I can do all things through Christ which strengtheneth me." (Phillipians 4:13)

These and other promises in the Bible not only provide encouragement, but provide information/concepts upon which one can meditate to help combat negative and self-destructive thoughts.

Another benefit of reading the Bible is that it enhances brain functioning. The relationship between the frontal lobe and depression has only been recently recognized in the scientific/medical world.[7] It has been found that when the functioning of the frontal lobe is enhanced, this reduces depression. Most of the healthy lifestyle practices that have been discussed in this booklet will improve frontal lobe functioning. There are also other lifestyle habits that can have a positive impact on our frontal lobes, one of which is the study of the Bible. Many have heard the saying, "If you don't use it, you will lose it." Any activity that is mentally challenging and stimulates us to use our reasoning ability is a form of "exercise" for our brains, and is especially helpful for frontal lobe functioning. Bible study, and not mere Bible *reading*, is one such activity. By the way, there are additional activities that can enhance frontal lobe functioning, which include singing and listening to hymns and/or classical music, eliminating entertainment TV viewing, and studying nature *(for further information on this, please consult Dr. Nedley's book, Depression: The Way Out)*.

Prayer, Meditation, and Depression

An increasing number of health professionals are recognizing that prayer and meditation can be beneficial for depression. For example, Dr. Martin Seligman, former president of the American Psychological Association, believes prayer helps with recovery from depression because it focuses the mind on things to be grateful for in life.[8] The type of prayer/meditation that is most beneficial is that which is focused on knowing who God is and what He wants from us and for us. This type of meditation is active and enhances brain functioning, especially the frontal lobe.[9] This is in contrast to Eastern-based mediation which may provide relaxation, but bypasses the frontal lobe because it encourages subjects to enter a trance-like state.[10] Also, with this latter type of meditation the focus is on self, rather than God.

PRACTICAL APPLICATION

If you are a person who does not have a history of religious involvement and would like to incorporate spirituality into your program for overcoming depression, here are a few suggestions:

1) Read the Bible on a daily basis. You may want to start out with the gospels that relate stories about Christ, who was a "human" representation of God. You could also include the daily reading of Proverbs. This book provides practical information to enhance mental, physical, and spiritual health. In addition, the "mental" effort needed to understand Proverbs will enhance frontal lobe functioning.[11]

2) If you can, obtain a copy of an inspired book about the life of Christ entitled, *The Desire of Ages* by E. G. White. This can be read in conjunction with the reading of the gospels in the New Testament.

3) Commune with God through prayer. Even if praying is awkward for you, try to do it in the best way that you can. The more you practice it, the more comfortable you will feel doing it.

4)   Become involved with a group of individuals who have spiritual interests. Of course, the simplest way to do this would be to join a church. For some, the thought of this may elicit negative feelings, for whatever reason. If you are not ready at this time to do so, at least keep it in mind for the near future!

5)   Whether or not you decide to join a church, consider finding a spiritually-grounded person with whom you can talk to about spiritual things.
*** As a cautionary note, don't try to use this person as a substitute for developing your own spiritual experience. Just consider him or her as a source of support as you try to grow spiritually.

6)   Read and memorize various Bible promises. This will not only provide encouragement, but will also be a good form of "exercise" for the brain.

CHAPTER 12

FINAL WORDS

The purpose of this booklet has been to share some simple, but powerful principles that can be used to treat depression. There are cases where it is necessary to consult medical or mental health experts for help with this illness. In fact, it is advised that before starting a program on your own, you should first consult a health-care professional for an evaluation of your condition to determine if any of these recommendations should be approached with caution. The nice thing about this approach is that it is a form of true "self-help" because it can prevent those who are depressed from over-reliance on medical or mental health professionals.

Let us review the eight lifestyle principles and how they can help with depression:

Nutrition—there are "key" nutrients that can reduce depression when added to the diet. These include omega-3 fatty acids, foods that contain trytophan, healthy carbohydrates, and even some vitamins (such as B-vitamins).

Exercise—there is evidence that exercise is helpful for depression because it increases serotonin, reduces stress/anxiety, and releases endorphins.

Water—the use of water internally hydrates the brain cells and removes poisons, which enhances brain functioning. The use of water externally can also help with depression in that it enhances the functioning of the nervous and circulatory systems of the body.

Sunshine—daily, moderate exposure to the sun will enhance mood and sleep.

Temperance—learning how to avoid harmful substances, such as caffeine, alcohol, and nicotine, and how to engage in healthy activities or ingest healthy substances in a balanced manner, can be very beneficial for overcoming depression.

Air—exposure to fresh air on a regular basis and learning how to breathe properly improves brain functioning, which can improve depression.

Rest—getting adequate sleep at the right time of night will provide many benefits that will help reduce depression.

Trust in Divine Power—developing a firm trust/faith in God and engaging in Bible reading/study, prayer, and active meditation is essential for a complete recovery from depression.

Some of you may be overwhelmed at this time, wondering how you are going to put all these principles into practice. One suggestion may be to work on each of these eight areas ONE AT A TIME. Start with the lifestyle principle that is the least difficult and work up to the more difficult ones. After a couple of months, you may feel strong enough to work on two areas at a time. Pace and do not overwhelm yourself. However, try to find a good balance between this and challenging yourself—remember, mental challenge helps your brain functioning, which can help with your depression.

It is my hope and prayer that as you put these principles into practice, you will see that they work! Believe it or not, depression can be cured! You do not have to be dependent on drugs or counseling for the rest of your life (or for a long period of your life). Give these strategies a try. You will be pleasantly surprised at the results!

NOTES

Chapter 1

1. American Psychiatric Association: *Diagnostic and statistical manual of mental disorders* (4ᵗʰed.). Washington, DC, American Psychiatric Association, 1994.

2. Ibid.

3. National Institute of Mental Health. The Numbers Count: Mental Disorders in America. Update from the National Institute of Mental Health. Bethesda (MD): National Institute of Mental Health, National Institutes of Health, US Department of Health and Human Services; 2006. 7 pages. Available from: http://www.nimh.nih.gov/publicat/numbers.cfm

4. World Health Organization. (2001). The World Health Report 2001—Mental Health: New Understanding, New Hope. Geneva World Health Organization.

5. Olfson, M., Marcus, S.C., Druss, B. et al. National trends in the outpatient treatment of depression. (2002). *Journal of the American Medical Association*, 287, 203–09.

Chapter 2

1. Nedley, N. *Depression Recovery Program DVD Series*. (2005). Ardmore, OK: Nedley Publishing.

Chapter 3

1. White, E. G. (1976). *Counsels on Diet and Foods* (p. 301). Hagerstown, MD: Review and Herald Publishing Association.

Chapter 4

1. White, E. G. (1977). *Mind, Character, and Personality*, Vol. 1 (p. 235). Hagerstown, MD: Review and Herald Publishing Association.

2. White, E. G. (1942). *Ministry of Healing* (p. 295). Boise, ID: Pacific Press Publishing Association.

3. Nedley, N. (2001). *Depression: The Way Out* (p. 66). Ardmore, OK: Nedley Publishing.

4. Talbot, P. and Cooper, S. (2006). Anterior cingulated and subgenual prefrontal blood flow changes following trytophan depletion in healthy males. *Neuropsychopharmacology*, (8), 1757–67.

5. Natural Antidepressants. Available from http://www. healthandnutrion.co.uk/articles/depression.htm.

6. Thomson, E. (2004). Carbs are essential for effective dieting and good mood. Massachusetts Institute of Technology – News Office.

7. Blackman, J., Towle, V., et al. (1990). Hypoglycemic thresholds for cognitive dysfunction in humans. *Diabetes*, 39(7), 828–835.

8. Edwards, R., Peet, M., Shay, J., Horrobin, D. (1998). Omega-3 polyunsaturated fatty acid levels in the diet and in the red blood cell membranes of depressed patients. *Journal of Affective Disorders*, 48, 149–55.

9. Parker, G., Gibson, N. (2006). Omega-3 fatty acid levels and mood disorders. *American Journal of Psychiatry*, 163. 969–978.

10. Adams, P., Lawson, S, et al. (1996). Arachidonic to eicosapentaenoic acid ratio in blood correlates positively with clinical symptoms of depression. *Lipids*, 31, 167–176.

11. Physicians Committee for Responsible Medicine, Washington, DC. Essential Fatty Acids (Fact Sheet). Available from http://animalliberationfront.com.

12. Alpert, J., Fava, M. (1997). Nutrition and depression: the role of folate. *Nutrition Reviews*, 55. 145–9.

13. Morris, M. (2003). Depression and folate status in the US Population. *Psychotherapy and Psychosomatics*, 72, 80–7.

14. Papakostas, G., Petersen, G., et al. (2004). Serum folate, vitamin B12, and Homocysteine in major depressive disorder, Part2: predictors of relapse during the continuation phase of pharmacotherapy.

15. Reynolds, E. H. (2002). Folic acid, ageing, depression, and dementia. *British Medical Journal*, 324, 1512–1515.

16. Fava, M., Borus, J., et al. (1997). Folate, vitamin B12, and homocysteine in major depressive disorder. *The American Journal of Psychiatry*, 154, 426–8.

17. Alpert, J., Fava, M. (1997). Nutrition and depression: the role of folate. *Nutrition Reviews*, 55, 145–9.

18. Pamplona-Roger, G. D. (2005). *Encyclopedia of Foods and Their Healing Power*, Vol. 2 (p. 30). Madrid, Spain: Editorial Safeliz, S.L.

18. Penninx, B., Guralnik, J., et al. (2000). Vitamin B12 deficiency and depression in physically disabled older women: epidemiologic evidence from the women's health and aging study. *American Journal of Psychiatry*, 157, 715–721.

19. Balch, J. (1997). *Prescription for Nutritional Healing* (p. 235). Garden City Park, NY: Avery Publishing Group.

Chapter 5

1. Blumenthal, J., et al. (1999). Effects of exercise training on older patients with major depression. *Archives of Internal Medicine*, 159, 2349–2356.

2. Dimeo, F., Bauer, M, et al. (2001). Benefits from aerobic exercise in patients with major depression. *The British Journal of Sports Medicine*, 35, 114–117.

3. Vickers-Douglas, K. (2006). Depression and anxiety: Exercise eases symptoms. Mayo Clinic Newsletter.

4. Nedley, N. (2001). *Depression: The Way Out* (p. 151). Ardmore, OK: Nedley Publishing.

Chapter 6

1. Lee, C. (1997). Understanding the Body Organs and the Eight Laws of Health (pp. 79–80). Brushton, NY: TEACH Services, Inc.

2. Mitchell, C. (2003). Mind and Body Relationship. *Adventists Affirm* (p. 17).

3. Thrash, A. and Thrash, C. (1981). *Home Remedies* (p. 6). Seale, AL: Thrash Publications.

4. Nedley, N. (2005). *Depression Recovery Program Workbook* (p. 47). Ardmore, OK: Nedley Publishing.

Chapter 7

1. Lambert, G., Reid, C., Kaye, D. M., et al. (2002). Effect of sunlight and season on serotonin turnover in the brain. *Lancet.* 360, 1840–1842.

2. Nedley, N.. (2001). *Depression: The Way Out* (p. 86). Ardmore, OK: Nedley Publishing.

3. Eastman, C., Young, M., et al. (1998). Bright light treatment of winter depression. *Archives of General Psychiatry,* 55, 883–889.

4. Kripke, D. (1998). Light treatment for nonseasonal depression: speed, efficacy and combined treatment. *Journal of Affective Disorders* 49, 109–117.

5. Golden, R., Bradley, G., et al. (2005). The efficacy of light therapy in the treatment of mood disorders; a review and meta-analysis of the evidence. *American Journal of Psychiatry,* 162, 656–662.

Chapter 8:

1. White, E. G. (1977). *Mind, Character, and Personality,* Vol. 2 (p. 394). Hagerstown, MD: Review and Herald Publishing.
2. Random House Dictionary. (1978). New York: Ballantine Books.

3. White, E.G. (1949). *Temperance*. (p. 76). Nampa, ID: Pacific Press Publishing Association.

4. White, E.G. (1981–1983). *Manuscript Releases,* Vol. 20 (p. 4). Hagerstown, MD: Review and Herald Publishing Association.

5. Pietraszek, M., Urana T, et al. (1991). Alcohol-induced depression: involvement of serotonin. *Oxford Journals*, 26, 155–159.

6. Missa, A. Mc-Allister-Williams. (2006). Alcohol and Depression. Available from http://www.netdoctor.co.uk.

7. Ibid.

8. Driessen, M., Veltrup, C., et al. (1998). Psychiatric co-morbidity, suicidal behavior, and suicidal ideation in alcoholics seeking treatment. *Addiction*, 93, 889–894.

9. Breslau, N., Kilbey, M, Andreski, P. (1994). DSM-III-R nicotine dependence in young adults: prevalence, correlates and associated psychiatric disorders. *Addiction*, 89, 743–754.

10. Breslau, N., Novak, S., Kessler, R. (2004). Psychiatric disorders and stages of smoking. *Biological Psychiatry*, 55, 69–76.

11. Windle, M. and Windle, R. (2001). Depressive symptoms and cigarette smoking among middle adolescents: prospective associations, and intrapersonal and interpersonal influences. *Journal of Consulting and Clinical Psychology*, 69, 215–26.

12. Nedley, N. (2001). *Depression: The Way Out* (p. 196). Ardmore, OK: Nedley Publishing.

13. Jacobsen B., Hansen V. (1988). Caffeine and health. *British Medical Journal*, 23, 291.

14. Kawachi, I., Willet, W., et al. (1996). A prospective study of coffee drinking and suicide in women. *Archives of Internal Medicine*, 156, 521–5.

15. Adapted from Hardinge, M., and Shyrock, H. (1991). *Family Medical Guide To Health and Fitness, Vol. 1* (p. 381, 382). Nampa,

ID: Pacific Press Publishing Association and Hagerstown, MD: Review & Herald Publishing Association.

Chapter 9:

1. White, E. G. *Mind, Character, and Personality*, Vol. 1 (p. 116). Hagerstown, MD: Review and Herald Publishing Association.

2. Thayer, R. E. (1989). *Biopsychology of Mood and Arousal.* New York: Oxford University Press.

3. Terman, M. and Terman, J. S. (1995). Treatment of seasonal affective disorder with a high output negative ionizer. *Journal of Alternative and Comparative Medicine*, 1, 87–92.

4. Buckalew, L, Rizzuto, A. (1982). Subjective response to negative air ion exposure. *Aviation, Space and Environmental Medicine*, 53, 822–823.

5. Jackson, T., and Jackson, L. *M.E.E.T. Ministry Handbook.* Huntingdon, TN.

Chapter 10

1. White, E.G. *Manuscript Releases*, Vol. 9 (p.169). Hagerstown, MD: Review and Herald Publishing Association.

2. Ford, D., Kamerow, D. (1989). Epidemiologic study of sleep disturbances and psychiatric disorders: An opportunity for prevention? *Journal of American Medical Association*, 262, 1479–1484.

3. White, E. G. *Manuscript Releases*, Vol. 7 (p. 224).

4. Ibid, Vol. 11 (p. 204).

5. Ohayon, M., et al. (2003). The effects of breathing-related sleep disorders on mood disturbances in the general population. *Journal of Clinical Psychiatry*, 64, 1195–2000.

Chapter 11

1. Kendler K., Gardner C., Prescott C. (1997). Religion, psychopathology, and substance use and abuse; a multimeasure, genetic-epidemiologic study. *American Journal of Psychiatry*, 154, 322–329.

2. Koenig H., George L., Peterson B. (1998). Religiosity and remission of depression in medically ill older patients. *American Journal of Psychiatry*, 55, 536–542.

3. Miller, L. et al. (1997). Religiosity and depression: ten-year follow-up of depressed mothers and offspring. *Journal of the American Academy of Child and Adolescent Psychiatry*, 36, 1416–1425.

4. Koenig, H., George, L, Peterson. (1998).

5. Fehring, R., Miller, J., Shaw, C. (1997). Spiritual well-being, religiosity, hope, depression, and other mood states in elderly people coping with cancer. *Oncology Nursing Forum*, 24, 663–671.

6. Random House Dictionary. (1978). New York: Ballantine Books.

7. Nedley, N. (2001). *Depression: The Way Out* (p. 176). Ardmore, OK: Nedley Publishing.

8. Easterbrook, G. Can you pray your way to health? Available from http://www.beliefnet.com/story/69/story_6991_1.html.

9. Nedley, N. *Depression: The Way Out* (p. 165).

10. Ibid, p. 166.

11. Nedley, N. (2005). *Depression Recovery Program DVD Series*. Ardmore, OK: Nedley Publishing.

We'd love to have you download our catalog of
titles we publish at:

www.TEACHServices.com

or write or email us your thoughts,
reactions, or criticism about this
or any other book we publish at:

TEACH Services, Inc.
254 Donovan Road
Brushton, NY 12916

info@TEACHServices.com

or you may call us at:

518/358-3494